WESTENDERS

Annie Tempest

FREDERICK MULLER
London Melbourne Auckland Johannesburg

First published in Great Britain in 1988 by
Frederick Muller, an imprint of
Century Hutchinson Ltd, Brookmount House, 62–65 Chandos Place,
London WC2N 4NW

Century Hutchinson Australia Pty Ltd
PO Box 496, 16–22 Church Street, Hawthorn, Victoria 3122, Australia

Century Hutchinson New Zealand Limited
PO Box 40–086, Glenfield, Auckland 10, New Zealand

Century Hutchinson South Africa (Pty) Ltd
PO Box 337, Bergvlei, 2021 South Africa

ISBN 0 09 173570 X

British Library Cataloguing in Publication Data

Tempest, Annie
 Westenders.
 1. English humorous cartoons. Collections
 from individual artists
 I. Title
 741.5′942

ISBN 0 09 173570 X

Printed in Great Britain by
Richard Clay Ltd, Bungay, Suffolk

To Mary and Geoffrey Stocker

Yuppy, aristocrat, free-loader, insider dealer . . .

By the time you grow up mummies and daddies will be test-tubes and pipettes.

Either of you two know where I put the Alkaseltzer?

I don't normally pick up hitch-hikers.

A delightful en suite bathroom featuring a Perrier-fed jacuzzi . . .

It's a party political broadcast . . .

Is that you darling?

My, Hamish! How you've grown!

Hamish's new Filofax has a condom wallet!

Now stop threatening to spank me Nanny – I'm old enough to enjoy it now.

Another one off to London to become a yuppy.

Mine's a real wally too – let's drop them both at Tattenham Corner.

In lay terms, she's a spoilt brat.

I've taken to jogging away from my responsibilities . . .

Gravy?

I find tapes of Prince Charles better than compost.

PHYSIOTHERAPY

And has that stiff upper lip been giving you any trouble lately?

For safety reasons the Royal Family never fly together.

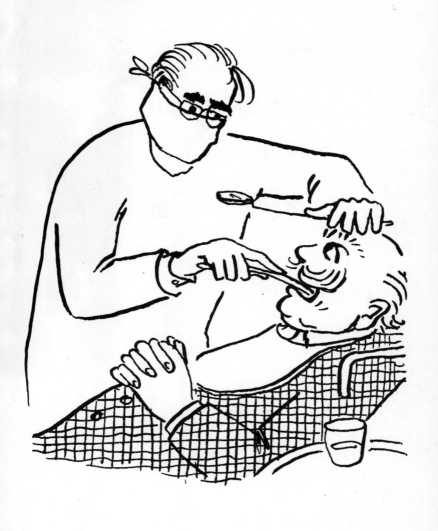

I see from your latest magazines that Asquith and Lloyd-George are at loggerheads again.

I've seen 700 of my closest friends and not a single horse.

Off with the TV darling – the snooker's over.

I'm getting confidential calls on my pace-maker and my heart-beat on my car 'phone.

The last of the '78, my Lord.

I was a communist once – then Daddy hit me.

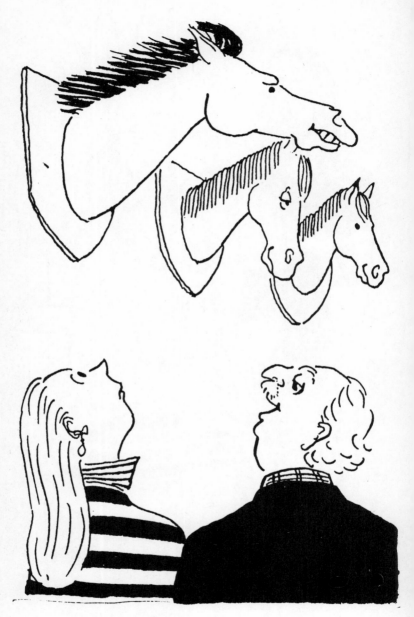

Gallipoli was very fast, you know.

More butter-ball than puff-ball.

No way Geoffrey! I draw the line at being rescued by the Grosslee-Thickets.

The future of the SDP? Let me see . . .

It may well be the latest thing, but I never wear anything that will frighten the horses.

It's all the rest of the field ever saw of Golden Fleece.

Insider dealing – isn't that when one's broker actually knows what he's talking about?

What luck! It's that bitch I met here last year.

I see the umpires are entering into the spirit of things this year.

Pepper?

. . . and, darling, I want my tiara out of the safe deposit box and back in Nanny's old biscuit tin.

Inform her ladyship of my headache, Blandford.

Of course we'll be getting our junior portable 'phone very soon.

Scotts Oyster Bar

Heavens! How did one of my pearls get in here?

Shirley may be fast, dear, but she has absolutely no *breeding.*

I suppose, in a way, you could say I was part of 'High' Society.

. . . and never whiten my doorstep again . . .

. . . and if any strange men wearing red roses like this come and try to kiss you – bite them.

Nanny says, if you have a moment, could you glance through her off-shore portfolio?

Polo types always dance as if they're treading in the divots.

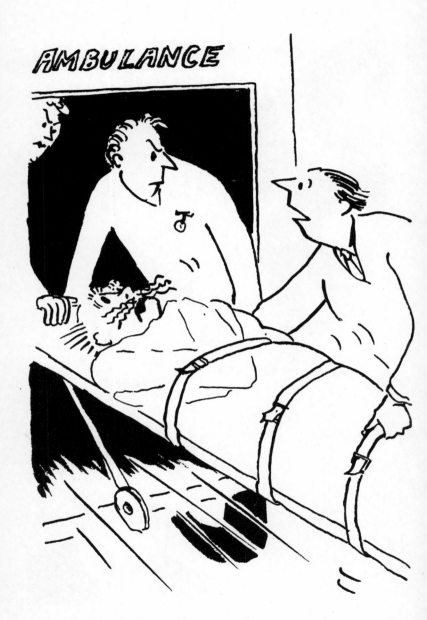

The TV broke down just as the Derby started.

Not everybody *drinks their whisky from a decanter, darling.*

He only heels to Gucci.

I've got to get him back to Moss Bros by midday.

Nothing that a lick of magnolia can't cure.

I think in future, Fiona, you might let Blandford pour the sherry for your friends.

I'm trying to give them up – have you got any crack?

Rumour has it that it's a safari park as well.

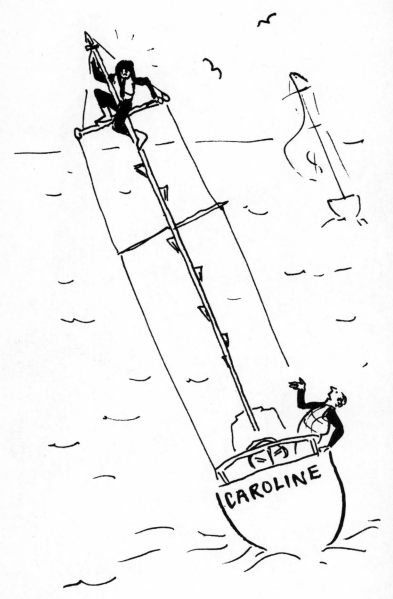

Fiona! If you come down I promise to name the next one after you.

I'll have you know that before I was a Hooray Henry, I was nothing.

He may be a penniless Irish drunk, but he's a member of all the best night-clubs in London.

I find the rain at Goodwood makes my hair go frizzy.

Nanny's still very protective.

Looks like another ex-junkies' party – I can only see Lucozade and Perrier.

You owe me a tenner, Jamie, I got her down the aisle.

. . . and Roger is signalling that he'd love to have you to stay too . . .

I had my tailor put in a poacher's pocket for my Filofax.

I thought you said you new boyfriend was au fait *with shooting.*

Good dinner at your club last night, darling?

I think he wants to be a politician when he grows up.

Rape and murder, nothing! I was done for fishing downstream on the Test.

Darling – number 13 across is 'antagonise'.

Not Lymeswold again!

Even money she'll be airborne with the next gust.

If Peregrine were my son I'd have him gelded.

How are you taking to beagling, Blandford?

Seriously, darling, you've caught me in the middle of washing my hair.

The children have grown up so fast – Hamish has pranged his first Porsche and Fiona has gate-crashed her first Charity Ball.

Now that's what I call solvent abuse.

I see my son has adapted well to your going co-ed.

I may not be meek enough to inherit the Earth, but I'll settle for a sizeable chunk of Norfolk.

Green back and sides.

She must be at least a Guinness.

You only love me when you're drunk.

Of course I expect you to go through a socialist phase – but not *during
election week.*

We're totally self-sufficient now – we even do our own washing up.

It's the latest racing plate from Gucci.

You'll be assisting Dr Wilson in his pre-menstrual tension clinic.

I do think the Parsley-Figits overdo it a little.

Somehow, if it was a post-coital cigarette, I wouldn't mind . . .

Not watching video nasties again are you, Justin?

The only pleasure he's given me was 9 months before he was born.

OK mate – hand over your manorial titles.